THE (X) FILES™

CREATED BY CHRIS CARTER

Dead to the World

Writers
Stefan Petrucha • John Rozum

Artist
Charles Adlard

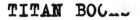

TITAN BOOKS

THE X-FILES: DEAD TO THE WORLD
ISBN 1 900097 24 9

Created by Chris Carter
Chapter heading illustrations by Miran Kim
Edited by Jim Salicrup and Dwight Jon Zimmerman

Published by Titan Books Ltd
42 — 44 Dolben St
London SE1 0UP

This book collects issues 1 — 3 of the Topps Comics series *The X-Files*
Comics Digest.

British Library Cataloguing-In-Publication data. A catalogue record
for this book is available from the British Library.

First edition: November 1996
10 9 8 7 6 5 4 3 2 1

Printed and bound in Great Britain by Stephens and George Ltd,
Merthyr Industrial Estate, Dowlais, Merthyr Tydfil.

THE Ⓧ FILES™

"DEAD TO THE WORLD"

Stefan Petrucha • Writer
Charles Adlard • Artist
John Workman • Letterer
George Freeman & Laurie E. Smith •
Colourists
Digital Chameleon • Separations

"BIG FOOT, WARM HEART"

Stefan Petrucha • Writer
Charles Adlard • Artist
John Workman • Letterer
George Freeman & Laurie E. Smith •
Colourists
Digital Chameleon • Separations

"SCAPE GOATS"

• John Rozum • Writer
Charles Adlard • Artist
John Workman • Letterer
George Freeman & Laurie E. Smith • Colourists
Digital Chameleon • Separations

OUT THERE...
ALREADY!

THE X-FILES:
FIREBIRD
£9.99 • ISBN 1 900097 08 7

THE X-FILES:
PROJECT AQUARIUS
£9.99 • ISBN 1 900097 17 6

THE X FILES™

JOSÉ AND ROSITA WILL NO DOUBT BE DUBBED ITS LATEST VICTIMS. I FIND IT DISHEARTENING THAT PEOPLE ARE SO QUICK TO BLAME SOME FANCIFUL MONSTER RATHER THAN ACCEPT A MORE TERRIBLE TRUTH.

IN MY EXPERIENCE, THERE IS ONLY ONE MONSTER WHICH CONTINUALLY PREYS ON HUMAN BEINGS; A MONSTER WHICH WILL NEVER STOP THIS TERRIBLE PRACTICE:

OTHER HUMAN BEINGS.

THE END

CARLOS SOTO HAS BEEN RELEASED FROM CUSTODY AND INTENDS TO USE HIS INHERITANCE TO ATTEND HARVAR[D] UNIVERSITY IN THE SPRING.

TESTS ON THE WIRE HANGER WER[E] INCONCLUSIVE, AND HECTOR WAS RELEASED AS WELL.

THE MURDERS REMAIN UNSOLVED, AS DOES THE MYSTERY OF WHATEVER'S KILLING THE ANIMALS OF PUERTO RICO.

THE CHUPACABRAS, WHETHER FERAL DO[G,] MONKEY, OR CREATURE PREVIOUSLY UNKNOWN, IS STILL AT LARGE, LURKI[NG] IN THE SHADOWS, PREYING ON THE ISLAND'S ANIMAL POPULATION, AND FEEDING ITS OWN GROWING MYTHOLOGY[.]

AUGUST 8, 1996
7:20 A.M.
ABOVE PUERTO RICO

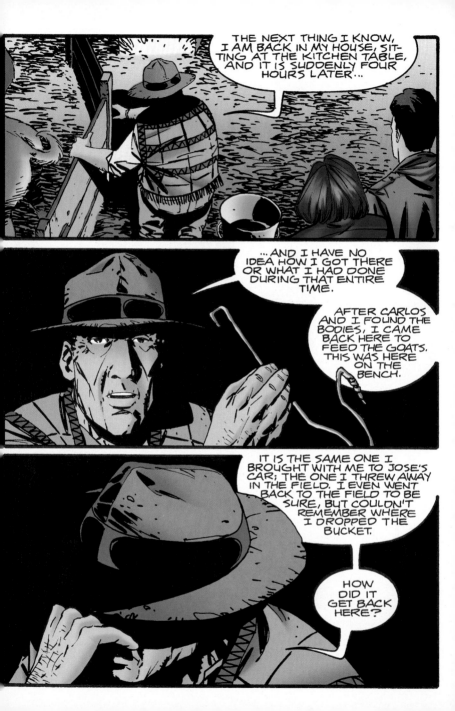

"AS I SAID, I PEERED IN THROUGH THE WINDOW WHEN I REACHED THE CAR. WHAT I WASN'T EXPECTING TO SEE WAS CARLOS'S GIRL-FRIEND ROSITA. SHE WAS JUST AS DRUNK AND ASLEEP AS JOSÉ.

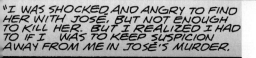

"I WAS SHOCKED AND ANGRY TO FIND HER WITH JOSÉ, BUT NOT ENOUGH TO KILL HER. BUT I REALIZED I HAD TO IF I WAS TO KEEP SUSPICION AWAY FROM ME IN JOSÉ'S MURDER.

"MY HEART WAS POUNDING WITH FEAR AND EXCITE-MENT OVER WHAT I WAS ABOUT TO DO. I REACHED FOR THE DOOR HANDLE TO THE CAR, KNOWING THERE WAS NO TURNING BACK.

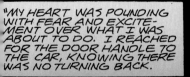

"THEN THE LIGHTS CAME.

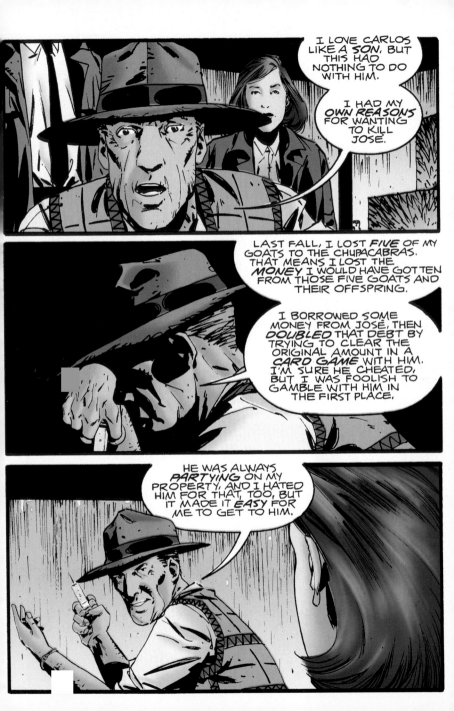

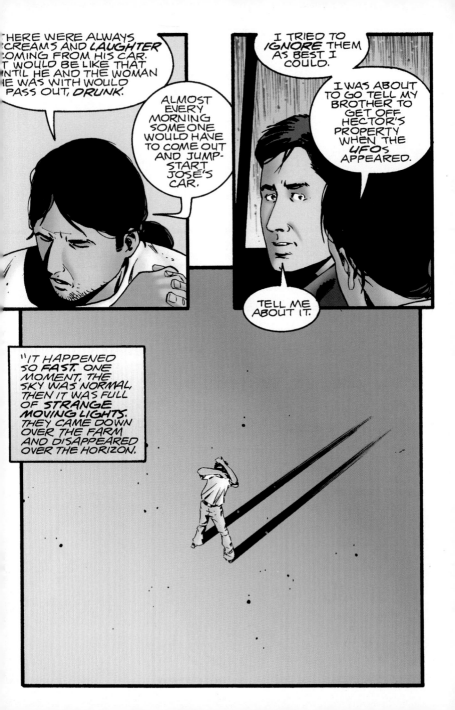

THERE WERE ALWAYS SCREAMS AND *LAUGHTER* COMING FROM HIS CAR. IT WOULD BE LIKE THAT UNTIL HE AND THE WOMAN HE WAS WITH WOULD PASS OUT, *DRUNK.*

ALMOST EVERY MORNING SOMEONE WOULD HAVE TO COME OUT AND JUMP-START JOSE'S CAR.

I TRIED TO *IGNORE* THEM AS BEST I COULD.

I WAS ABOUT TO GO TELL MY BROTHER TO GET OFF HECTOR'S PROPERTY WHEN THE *UFOS* APPEARED.

TELL ME ABOUT IT.

"IT HAPPENED SO *FAST.* ONE MOMENT, THE SKY WAS NORMAL, THEN IT WAS FULL OF *STRANGE MOVING LIGHTS.* THEY CAME DOWN OVER THE FARM AND DISAPPEARED OVER THE HORIZON.

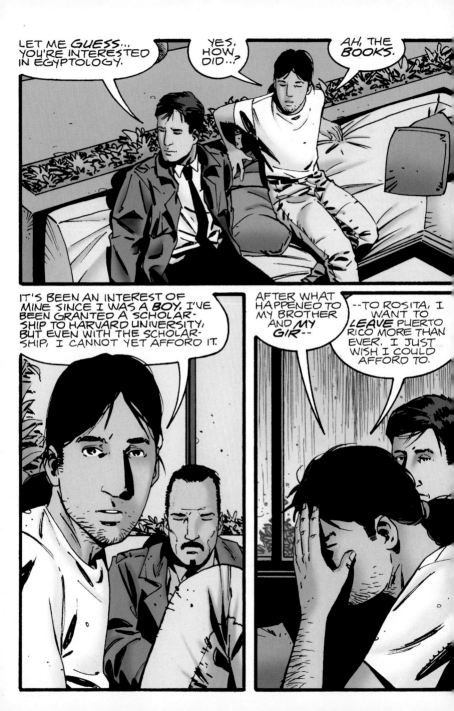

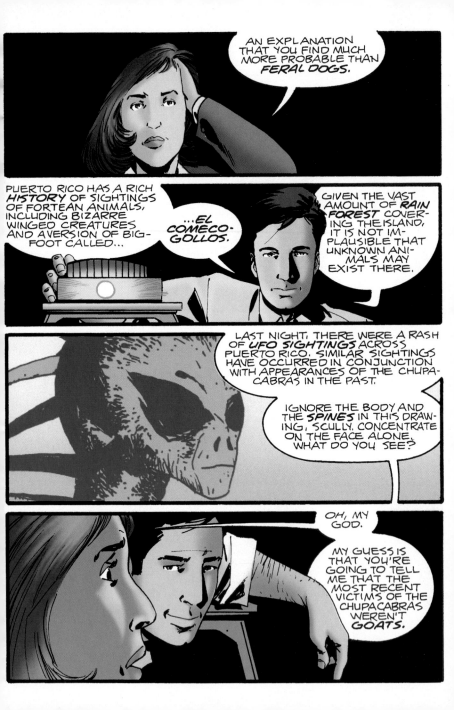

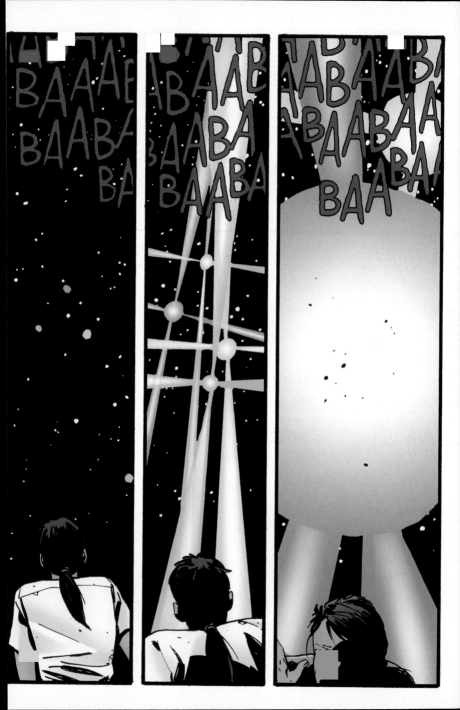

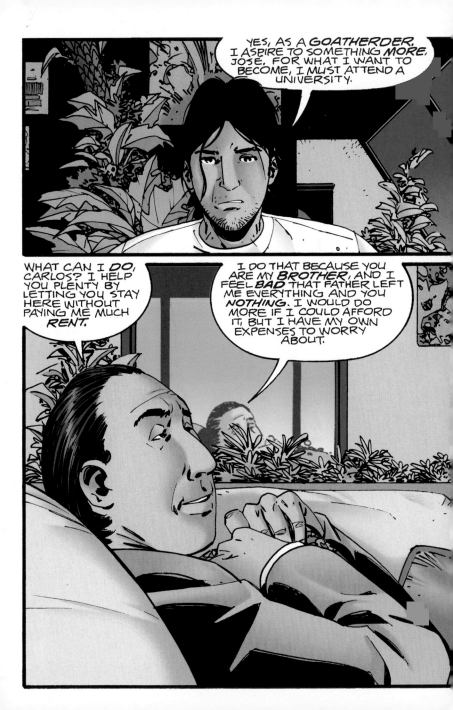

UHN.

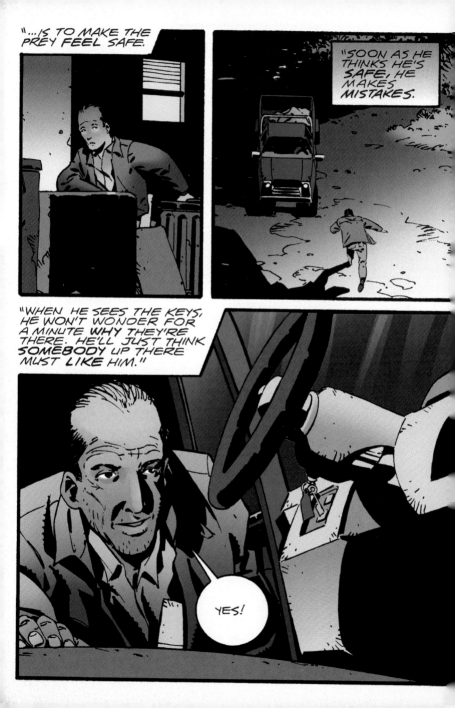

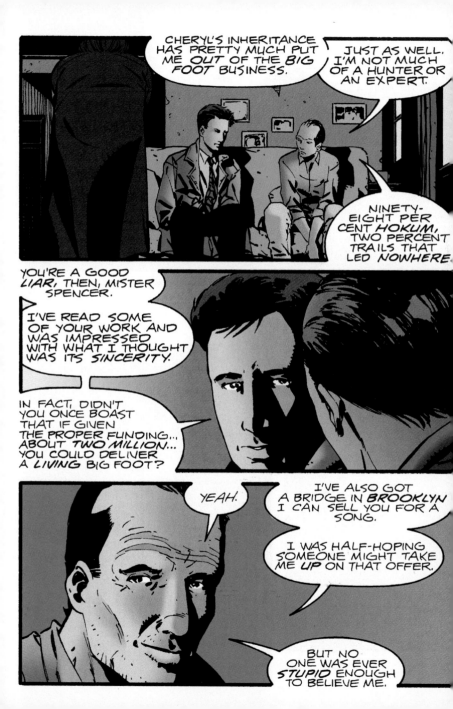

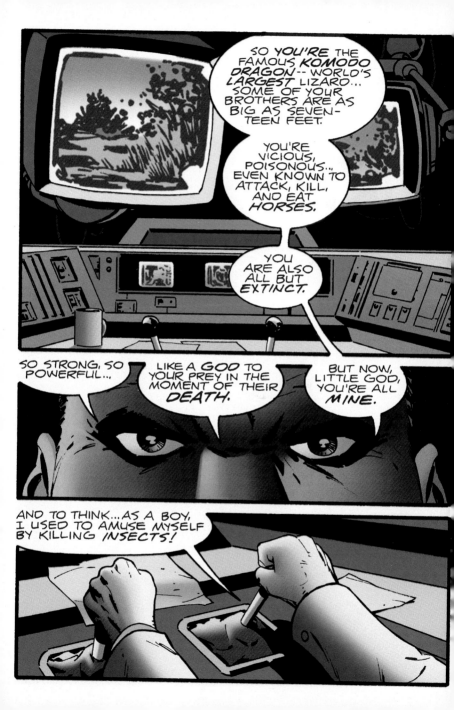

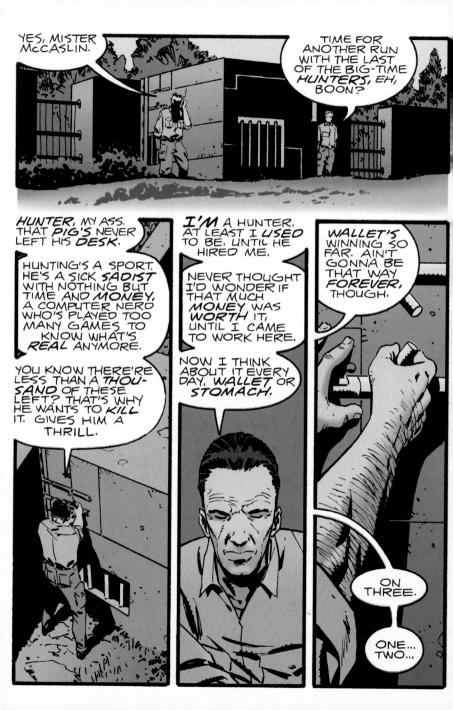

THIS IS WHERE THEY FOUND WHAT WAS LEFT OF WALTHAM'S CAMP.
GRAYS HARBOR COUNTY
WASHINGTON
TUESDAY
11:20 A.M.
TRACKS ARE FADING ALREADY.
I CAN TELL YOU THIS, THOUGH... BIG FOOT IS DEFINITELY NOT A MISNOMER.
RARK RAR RARK RAR
MULDER! LOOK OUT!

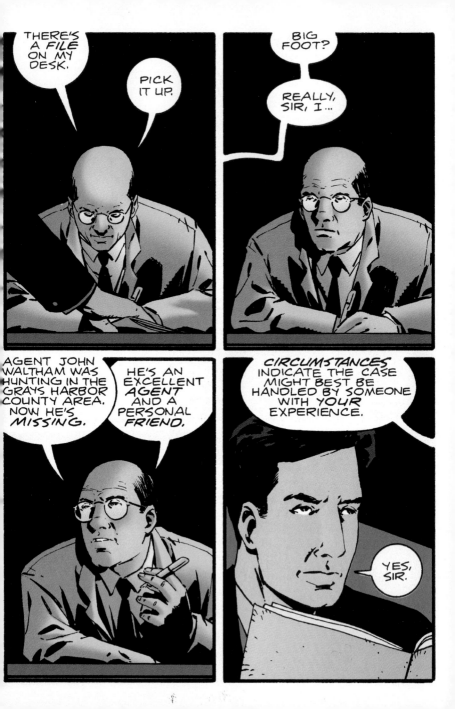

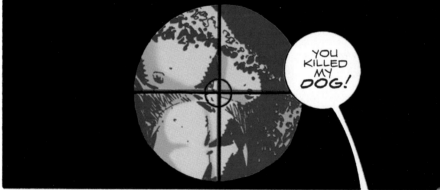

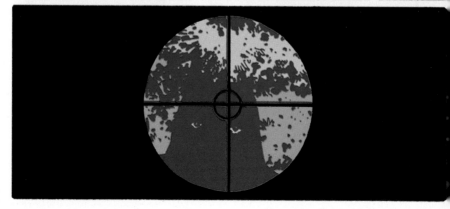

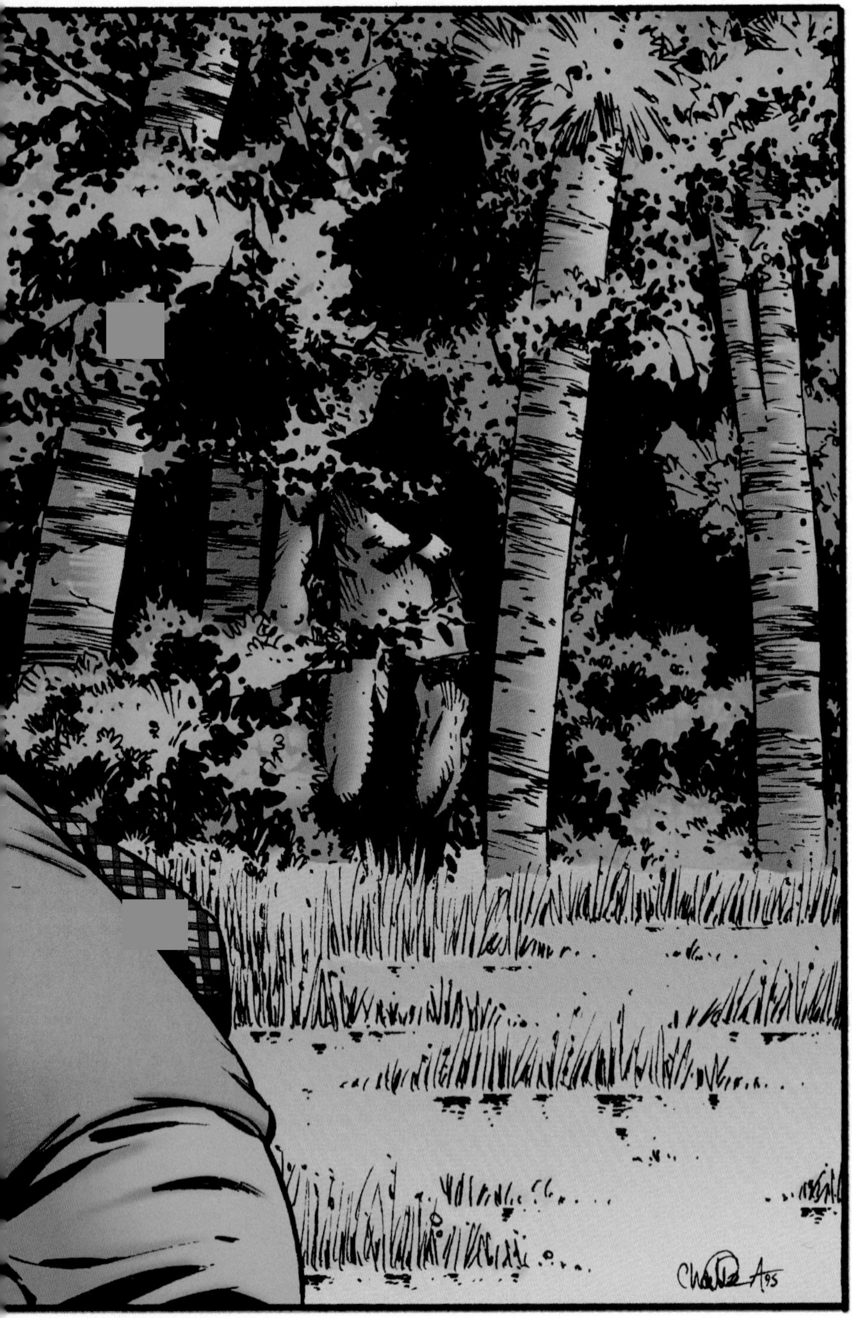

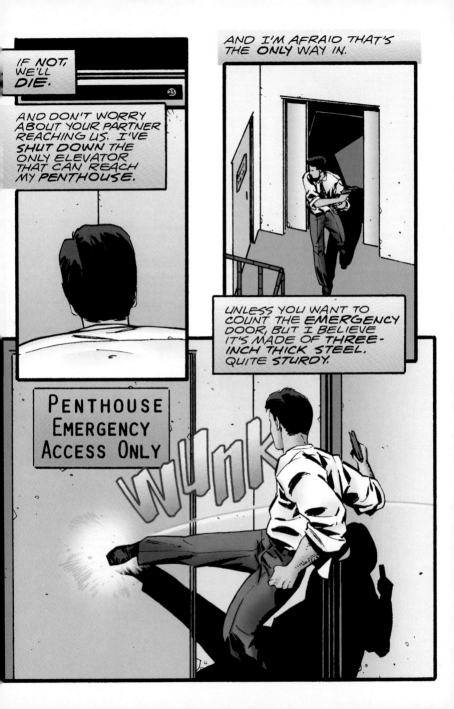

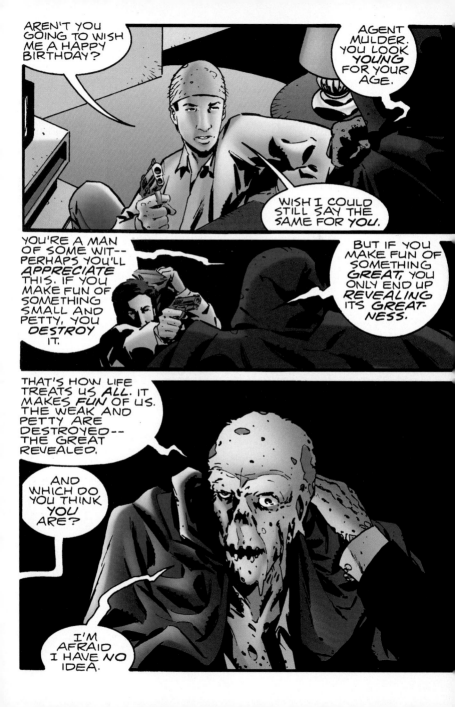

AGHHHHHHH!

NGGGGG!

11:40 P.M.
THE PONCE DE LEON RETIREMENT COMMUNITY

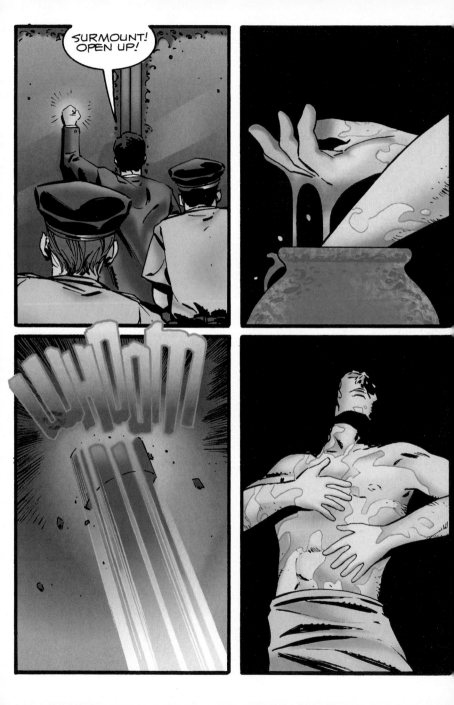

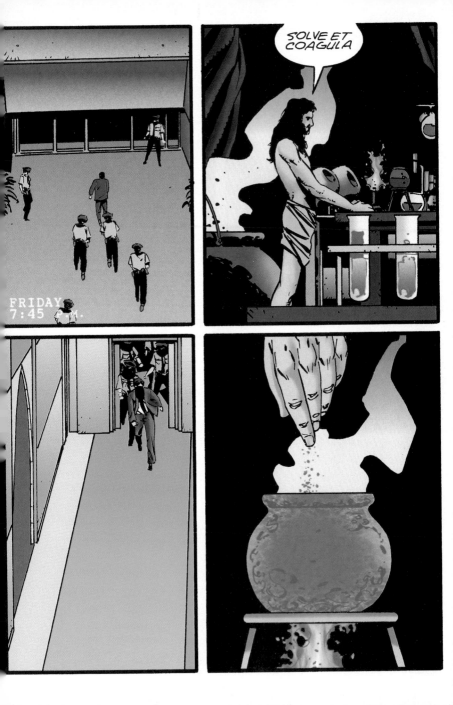

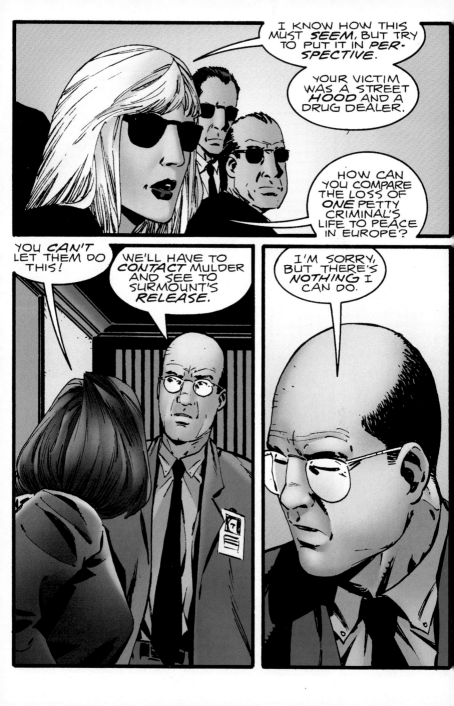

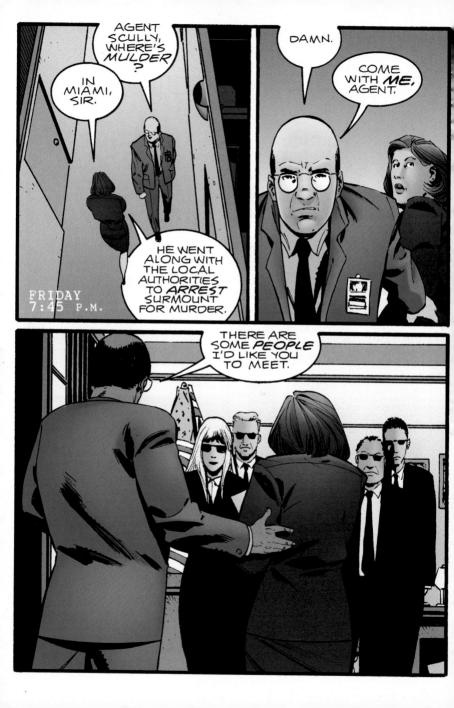

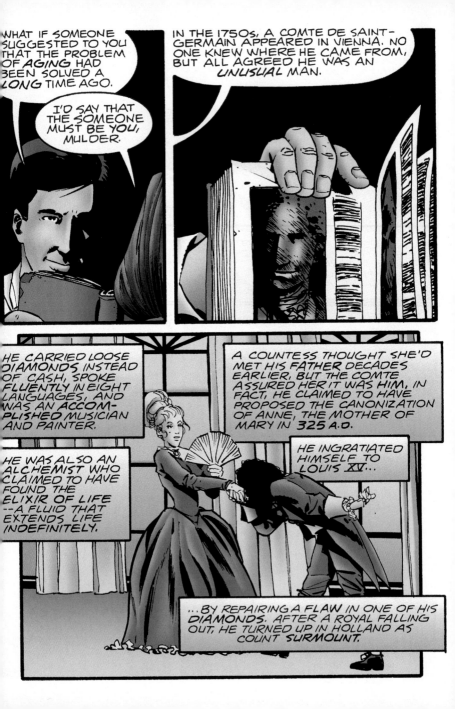

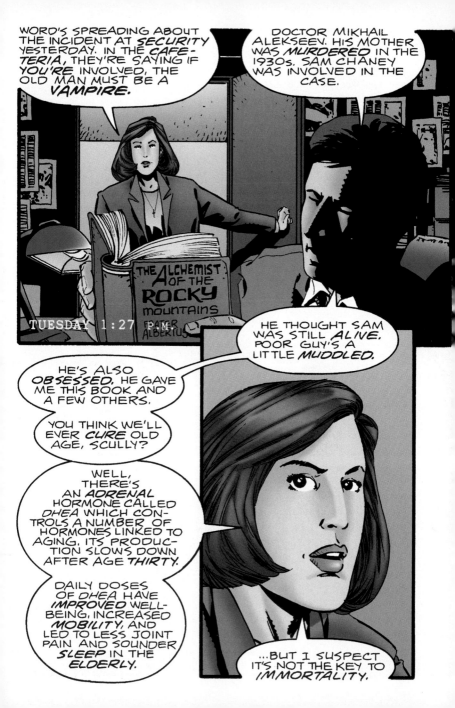

HELLO.

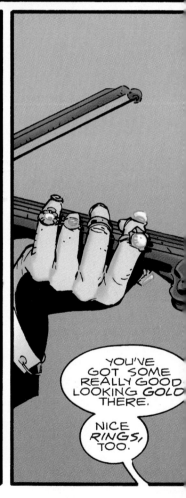

YOU'VE GOT SOME REALLY GOOD LOOKING *GOLD* THERE.

NICE *RINGS,* TOO.

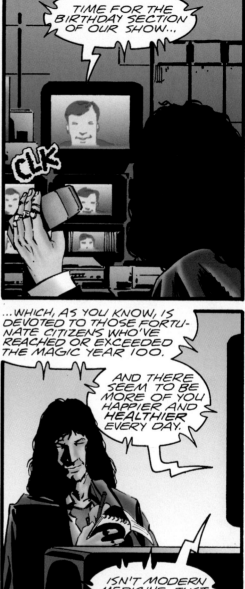

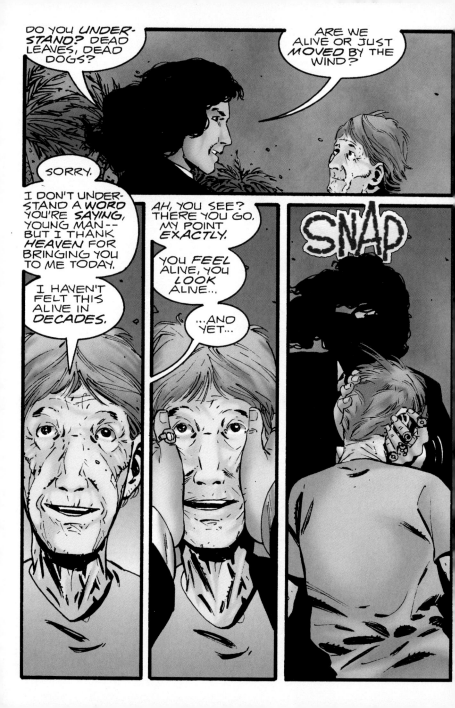